Fourth Edition

READING
FOR COMPREHENSION
Level B

Contributing writers: Andrea Leeds Clare, Susan J. Riddle,
Thomas Gunning, Susan McAlpine, Ellen Walpole
Cover Design: Nancy Tobin/Square Moon Productions
Interior design: Ada K. Hanlon

To the Student

This book has all kinds of fun stories for you to read. Some stories tell about strange animals. Some stories take you to special places. And some stories let you meet interesting people.

There are questions after each story. They will help you to think about and remember what you've read. That is why the book is called READING FOR COMPREHENSION. *Comprehension* means "understanding." Good readers understand what they read. This book can help you become a better reader.

ISBN 0-8454-2697-4

CONTINENTAL PRESS
Elizabethtown, PA 17022

Contents

Who was Mary McLeod Bethune?

1   Some days you may love school. Other days you might not. But suppose people wouldn't let you go to school. How would you learn? How would you feel?

2   That is what happened to young Mary McLeod Bethune. When she was growing up, African Americans couldn't go to schools with white people. And there were no schools for blacks near Mary's house.

3   Finally, a school opened up. Mary was 10 years old. At last she could learn to read. Mary loved learning. She went on to become a teacher. Then she started her own school to help others learn.

Mary McLeod Bethune

Fill in the circle (○) beside the right answer.

1. Mary McLeod Bethune became a _____.
   ○ teacher   ○ doctor   ○ farmer

2. This story tells about someone who loved to _____.
   ○ play   ○ spend money   ○ learn

3. In the first part of the story, what does the word *school* mean?
   ○ bunch of fish   ○ place for classes   ○ train a pet

4. Mary didn't learn to read until she was 10 because she _____.
   ○ wasn't smart enough   ○ couldn't go to school
               ○ didn't like learning

5. You can guess from the story that Mary _____.
   ○ learned fast   ○ was a bad teacher   ○ hated school

3

What is a walking stick?

1   A walking stick is a bug. But it looks like a stick. That is how it got its name.

2   A walking stick likes to eat leaves. It is safe in a tree. It looks like a twig that is part of the tree. Other animals don't see it.

3   A walking stick can also change color. It is green in the spring. In the fall, it is brown. This bug can hide itself very well.

walking stick

Fill in the circle (○) beside the right answer.

1. A walking stick likes to eat _____.
   - ○ birds
   - ○ leaves
   - ○ other bugs

2. This story mostly tells about how walking sticks _____.
   - ○ find food
   - ○ hide themselves
   - ○ make nests

3. In the third part of the story, what does the word *fall* mean?
   - ○ drop down
   - ○ a color
   - ○ a time of year

4. Other animals can't see the walking stick because it _____.
   - ○ flies away
   - ○ is a bug
   - ○ looks like part of a tree

5. You can guess from the story that the walking stick changes its color so that it can _____.
   - ○ get smaller
   - ○ look like a tree
   - ○ be seen well

READING FOR COMPREHENSION

Student Name _____Jayden_____

Circle the number of each question that you missed.

Page 3:	1	2	3	4	5	**Page 21:**	1	2	3	4	5	**Page 39:**	1	2	3	4	5
Page 4:	1	2	3	4	5	**Page 22:**	1	2	3	4	5	**Page 40:**	1	2	3	4	5
Page 5:	1	2	3	4	5	**Page 23:**	1	2	3	4	5	**Page 41:**	1	2	3	4	5
Page 6:	1	2	3	4	5	**Page 24:**	1	2	3	4	5	**Page 42:**	1	2	3	4	5
Page 7:	1	2	3	4	5	**Page 25:**	1	2	3	4	5	**Page 43:**	1	2	3	4	5
Page 8:	1	2	3	4	5	**Page 26:**	1	2	3	4	5	**Page 44:**	1	2	3	4	5
Page 9:	1	2	3	4	5	**Page 27:**	1	2	3	4	5	**Page 45:**	1	2	3	4	5
Page 10:	1	2	3	4	5	**Page 28:**	1	2	3	4	5	**Page 46:**	1	2	3	4	5
Page 11:	1	2	3	4	5	**Page 29:**	1	2	3	4	5	**Page 47:**	1	2	3	4	5
Page 12:	1	2	3	4	5	**Page 30:**	1	2	3	4	5	**Page 48:**	1	2	3	4	5
Page 13:	1	2	3	4	5	**Page 31:**	1	2	3	4	5	**Page 49:**	1	2	3	4	5
Page 14:	1	2	3	4	5	**Page 32:**	1	2	3	4	5	**Page 50:**	1	2	3	4	5
Page 15:	1	2	3	4	5	**Page 33:**	1	2	3	4	5	**Page 51:**	1	2	3	4	5
Page 16:	1	2	3	4	5	**Page 34:**	1	2	3	4	5	**Page 52:**	1	2	3	4	5
Page 17:	1	2	3	4	5	**Page 35:**	1	2	3	4	5	**Page 53:**	1	2	3	4	5
Page 18:	1	2	3	4	5	**Page 36:**	1	2	3	4	5	**Page 54:**	1	2	3	4	5
Page 19:	1	2	3	4	5	**Page 37:**	1	2	3	4	5	**Page 55:**	1	2	3	4	5
Page 20:	1	2	3	4	5	**Page 38:**	1	2	3	4	5	**Page 56:**	1	2	3	4	5

>>

Evaluation

Times Missed

Question 1: Recalling Details _____

Question 2: Using Context Clues _____

Question 3: Recognizing the Main Idea of a Paragraph _____

Question 4: Completing an Analogy Statement _____

Question 5: Understanding Multiple-Meaning Words or
Making Valid Inferences _____

>>

Summary

This student has mastered question types _____.

This student is having difficulty with question types _____.

Reading for Comprehension

Why do we yawn?

1   Sometimes people feel sleepy. They can't stay interested in what they are doing. Then they open their mouths wide. We call this a *yawn*. It makes a pretty silly face. Why do people do it?

2   Scientists do not know much about yawns. But they have some ideas. Our bodies get tired. Our minds get tired, too. A tired mind needs air. So we yawn. The quick yawn wakes up our mind. But not for long. Watch out! Here comes another yawn.

yawn

Fill in the circle (○) beside the right answer.

1. We yawn with our _____.
   ○ nose   ○ mouth   ○ ears

2. This story tells about what people do when they are _____.
   ○ asleep   ○ eating   ○ tired

3. In the first part of the story, what does the word *silly* mean?
   ○ funny   ○ pretty   ○ dark

4. People yawn in order to get more _____.
   ○ food   ○ sleep   ○ air

5. You can guess from the story that people do not stop yawning until they _____.
   ○ get some rest   ○ read a book   ○ get tired out

Can horses dance?

1   You know that horses can walk. You know that horses can jump. But do you know that some horses can dance?

2   The dancing horses live in Austria. They go to school there. People train the horses to do many things. The horses learn to stand on their back legs. They also learn to walk and jump to music.

3   People come from all over the world to see the white horses. The horses are beautiful. Their dances are beautiful, too.

dancing horse

Fill in the circle (○) beside the right answer.

1. The special horses live in _____.
   - ○ Austria
   - ○ the United States
   - ○ England

2. This story tells about horses that _____.
   - ○ race
   - ○ jump fences
   - ○ dance

3. In the third part of the story, what does the word *beautiful* mean?
   - ○ sad
   - ○ pretty
   - ○ slow

4. The horses can dance because _____.
   - ○ all horses can
   - ○ their legs are fat
   - ○ they learn in school

5. You can guess from the story that the dancing horses _____.
   - ○ are not very smart
   - ○ are fun to watch
   - ○ can stand on just their front legs, too

How is a piano like a drum?

1   A piano does not look like a drum. It does not sound like a drum, either. So how can the two be alike?

2   To play a drum, you use sticks. You hit the drum. Then sound comes out.

3   You play a piano in the same way. You hit the keys. The keys move hammers inside the piano. The hammers hit strings to make sounds. That is how a piano is like a drum.

piano

drum

Fill in the circle (○) beside the right answer.

1. To play a drum, you use _____.
   - ○ keys
   - ○ hammers
   - ○ sticks

2. This story tells how you _____ drums and pianos.
   - ○ make
   - ○ play
   - ○ carry

3. In the second part of the story, what does the word *play* mean?
   - ○ make music on
   - ○ be in a game
   - ○ a story on a stage

4. Drums and pianos are alike because _____ makes their sounds.
   - ○ hitting
   - ○ rubbing
   - ○ blowing

5. You can guess from the story that pianos _____ than drums.
   - ○ sound better
   - ○ cost less
   - ○ have more parts

123 456 789 10 11 12 13 14 15 16 17 18 19 20

What is a flying fox?

1   A flying fox is not a fox at all. It is a bat. But this bat has a face that looks like a fox.

2   A flying fox is the biggest bat. Its wings are 6 feet across. This bat likes to eat fruit. Sometimes the flying fox is called the "fruit bat."

3   The flying fox uses its eyes and nose to find fruit trees. Then it eats some of the fruit. Fruit farmers get angry. They do not like the flying fox.

flying fox

fruit

farmer

Fill in the circle (○) beside the right answer.

1. The flying fox likes to eat _____.
   - ○ foxes
   - ○ chickens
   - ○ fruit

2. This story tells mostly about a kind of _____.
   - ○ bat
   - ○ fox
   - ○ tree

3. In the first part of the story, what does the word *like* mean?
   - ○ love
   - ○ almost the same as
   - ○ not

4. Farmers don't like the flying fox because it _____.
   - ○ flies
   - ○ eats fruit from trees
   - ○ looks like a fox

5. You can guess from the story that farmers _____.
   - ○ feed flying foxes
   - ○ plant a lot of trees
   - ○ try to get rid of flying foxes

8

Who was Roberto Clemente?

1   Roberto Clemente was a great baseball star. He could jump high to catch a ball. He could run fast. And he could hit a ball really hard.

2   Roberto loved children. He wanted to build a park for the children of Puerto Rico.

3   In 1972, Roberto was killed in an airplane crash. But people did not forget him. They sent money for the children's park. It opened in 1975. Roberto Clemente's dream had come true.

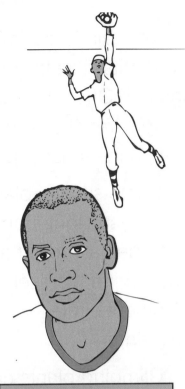

Roberto Clemente

Fill in the circle (○) beside the right answer.

1. Roberto Clemente was killed in ____.
   - ○ a car
   - ○ a baseball game
   - ● an airplane crash

2. This story tells about ____.
   - ● a kind baseball star
   - ○ Roberto Clemente's team
   - ○ poor children

3. In the first part of the story, what does the word *great* mean?
   - ● huge
   - ○ old
   - ● very, very good

4. Roberto wanted to build a park because he ____.
   - ○ wanted to play baseball
   - ● loved children
   - ○ was killed

5. You can guess from the story that people ____ Roberto's dream.
   - ○ fought
   - ● believed in
   - ○ didn't like

9

Can plants climb?

1   The rain forest is home to many trees and plants. The tall plants grow close together. Often the sunlight cannot get through. Yet all green plants need sunlight. How do the smaller plants find it?

2   Some smaller plants climb larger plants to reach sunlight. Some climbing plants have special roots that stick to tree trunks. Others wind themselves around the trees. Still others circle the trees with strong but tiny strings.

3   Climbing plants can be thin vines. Or they can be as wide as a rope. But they all are reaching for the sun.

climbing plants

Fill in the circle (○) beside the right answer.

1. Some climbing plants _____ tree trunks.
   ○ take bark off   ○ kill   ○ stick to

2. This story tells about plants that _____.
   ○ die   ○ are not green   ○ climb

3. In the first part of the story, what does the word *through* mean?
   ○ finished   ○ from top to bottom   ○ up

4. Climbing plants climb because they need _____.
   ○ sunlight   ○ water   ○ air

5. You can guess from the story that the rain forest floor is _____.
   ○ dark   ○ wet   ○ empty

How did ghost crabs get their name?

1   Ghost crabs live near the sea. They dig homes in the sand. These crabs can run very fast. Some people call them racing crabs.

2   Ghost crabs are the same color as the sand. This helps them to hide. The crabs are easy to see when they move. But they are hard to see when they are still. This is why some people call them ghost crabs.

ghost crab

Fill in the circle (○) beside the right answer.

1. Ghost crabs are the same color as the _____.
    ○ sea   ○ sand   ○ sky

2. This story tells how the ghost crab got its _____.
    ○ name   ○ home   ○ color

3. In the second part of the story, what does the word *still* mean?
    ○ the same as before   ○ part of a window   ○ not moving

4. Some people call these animals _____ crabs because they can run very fast.
    ○ ghost   ○ racing   ○ hiding

5. You can guess from the story that when ghost crabs want to hide they _____.
    ○ run very fast   ○ do not move   ○ close their eyes

Why do people ride in balloons?

1   Every year, hundreds of people go for rides in balloons. These big balloons fly high in the sky. They are pushed along by the wind.

2   A large basket hangs under each balloon. People ride in the basket. From there they can see the tops of houses and trees. The people, cars, and buildings on the ground look very small.

3   Some people take long trips in the big balloons. They visit new places and see new things. They like to sail high above the earth.

Fill in the circle (○) beside the right answer.

1. On a balloon ride, people ride _____.
   - ○ on the balloon   ○ in a basket   ○ in a car

2. This story tells mostly about _____.
   - ○ children's balloons   ○ big flying balloons   ○ the wind

3. In the third part of the story, what does the word *visit* mean?
   - ○ go to   ○ talk to   ○ move to

4. People on the ground look small because the balloon is _____.
   - ○ very big   ○ too close   ○ so high up

5. You can guess from the story that you can _____ in a balloon.
   - ○ not see the ground   ○ plant trees   ○ go very far

What are glassfish?

1   Glassfish are small fish. Some are light green. Some are yellow.

2   A glassfish looks like a piece of glass. You can see right through this fish. You can even see the bones inside its body.

3   Most glassfish live in the ocean. But some glassfish live in lakes or rivers. And some glassfish live in houses. People keep them as pets.

glassfish

>>>

Fill in the circle (○) beside the right answer.

1. Most glassfish live in _____.
   - ○ the ocean
   - ○ rivers
   - ○ houses

2. This story does not tell about _____.
   - ○ what glassfish look like
   - ○ what glassfish eat
   - ○ where glassfish live

3. In the second part of the story, what does the word *right* mean?
   - ○ next to
   - ○ always
   - ○ straight

4. The glassfish got its name because it looks like a piece of _____.
   - ○ fish
   - ○ bone
   - ○ glass

5. You can guess from the story that people like to _____ glassfish.
   - ○ eat
   - ○ look at
   - ○ hunt

>>>

How did zoos begin?

1   The first zoos started a long time ago. They belonged to kings and queens. You had to be rich to bring strange animals from far away places.

2   Later, zoos opened for everyone. But sometimes people did not take good care of the animals. There was not enough room to move around in their small cages.

3   Now many zoos have changed. The animals live in large, open parks. People watch them from cars and buses. These zoos are better for the animals. And they are still fun for people.

Fill in the circle (○) beside the right answer.

1. The first zoos started _____.
   - ○ last year
   - ○ long ago
   - ○ about 5 years ago

2. This story tells mostly about _____.
   - ○ kings
   - ○ cages
   - ○ zoos

3. In the first part of the story, what does the word *rich* mean?
   - ○ tasting good
   - ○ having a lot of money
   - ○ growing plants well

4. Today's zoos are better for the animals because the places are _____.
   - ○ large, open parks
   - ○ small cages
   - ○ still fun for people

5. You can guess from the story that animals are _____ in small cages.
   - ○ well cared for
   - ○ still
   - ○ unhappy

Can a flying squirrel really fly?

1   A flying squirrel cannot really fly like a bird. But it can sail through the air.

2   A flying squirrel has loose fur along its sides. It jumps from a tree. Then it opens its legs. Its loose fur stretches out like wings. And the flying squirrel sails to the ground or over to another tree.

3   This small animal lives in a hole in a tree. It comes out only at night to look for food.

flying squirrel

Fill in the circle (○) beside the right answer.

1. The flying squirrel lives in _____.
   - ○ ponds
   - ○ the ground
   - ○ trees

2. This story tells about a kind of _____.
   - ○ bird
   - ○ squirrel
   - ○ bat

3. In the second part of the story, what does the word *stretches* mean?
   - ○ sinks
   - ○ spreads
   - ○ strikes

4. The flying squirrel can sail through the air because it has loose _____ along its sides.
   - ○ feathers
   - ○ legs
   - ○ fur

5. You can guess from the story that the flying squirrel sleeps during the _____.
   - ○ night
   - ○ day
   - ○ summer

Do you know what to do in a fire?

1   Suppose a fire breaks out at your school. Do you know what to do? You should. If you don't, you could become frightened. You could lose your way and not be able to get out.

2   Most schools have you practice what to do in case of a fire. First of all, don't run. Line up in an orderly way. Then leave quietly. Be sure you know where all the doors in the school are. You may not be in your classroom when a fire starts.

3   It's important to practice at home, too. You can keep safe in a fire if you know what to do.

fire drill

Fill in the circle (○) beside the right answer.

1. If a fire happens, leave the building in an orderly and _____ way.
   - ○ noisy
   - ○ silly
   - ○ quiet

2. This story tells what to do if a _____ happens.
   - ○ flood
   - ○ fire
   - ○ car crash

3. In the first part of the story, what does the word *lose* mean?
   - ○ not find
   - ○ not win
   - ○ not tight

4. You should know what to do in a fire so that you don't get _____.
   - ○ sick
   - ○ tired
   - ○ frightened

5. You can guess from the story that people in _____ should also practice what to do if a fire breaks out.
   - ○ fields
   - ○ offices
   - ○ pools

16

How do mail carriers keep dogs away?

1 Mail carriers and dogs are not always good friends. Sometimes dogs bite. But mail carriers are doing something about this.

2 Some mail carriers use a whistle. The whistle makes a loud sound. Only dogs can hear it. They do not like it. So the dogs run away.

3 Other mail carriers take dog candy with them. They hope that dogs will like the candy. Then the dogs will not bite them.

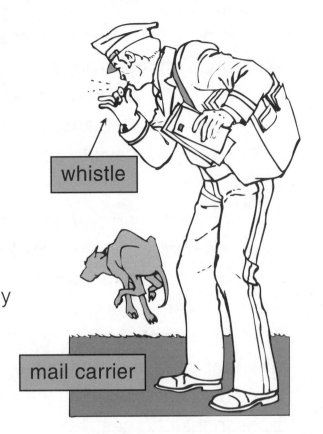

whistle

mail carrier

Fill in the circle (○) beside the right answer.

1. Sometimes dogs _____ mail carriers.
   - ○ kill
   - ○ break
   - ○ bite

2. This story tells about mail carriers and _____.
   - ○ caps
   - ○ letters
   - ○ dogs

3. In the second part of the story, what does the word *sound* mean?
   - ○ noise
   - ○ well
   - ○ bell

4. Dogs run away from a mail carrier's whistle because they _____.
   - ○ do not like it
   - ○ want the candy
   - ○ have to go home

5. You can guess from the story that mail carriers _____.
   - ○ work too hard
   - ○ meet a lot of dogs
   - ○ don't like any dogs

What are army ants?

1   Army ants walk in long lines through the forest. They are looking for food. Nothing seems to stop them. They go over large rocks. They even find ways to get across water.

2   Sometimes army ants go into people's homes. The people leave. They do not want the ants to bite them. At last, the ants move on. Then the people come back. They are happy that the ants came. The army ants have eaten all the other bugs in their homes.

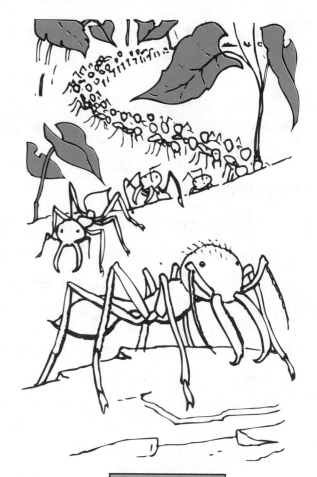

army ants

Fill in the circle (○) beside the right answer.

1. When army ants go into a home, the people _____.
   ○ make them pets   ○ leave   ○ give them food

2. This story tells about how army ants _____.
   ○ look and taste   ○ fly and swim   ○ move and eat

3. In the first part of the story, what does the word *rocks* mean?
   ○ stones   ○ ships   ○ moves from one side to the other

4. People are happy because the ants have eaten the _____ in their homes.
   ○ food   ○ bugs   ○ leaves

5. You can guess from the story that people are _____ army ants.
   ○ close to   ○ good to   ○ afraid of

Why do clowns go to school?

1 Most people go to school to learn to read and write. But some people go to school to learn to be clowns.

clown

2 At clown school, people learn many things. They learn how to dress in funny clothes. They learn how to paint their faces with bright colors. And they learn how to do silly tricks.

3 Clown school can be a lot of fun. But it is a lot of hard work, too.

Fill in the circle (O) beside the right answer.

1. At clown school, people learn how to paint their _face_.
   - ● faces
   - O houses
   - O clothes

2. This story tells about a special kind of _school_.
   - O trick
   - ● school
   - O paint

3. In the second part of the story, what does the word *many* mean?
   - O all
   - O a few
   - ● a lot

4. People go to these schools because they want to become _clowns_.
   - O doctors
   - O rich
   - ● clowns

5. You can guess from the story that clowns do silly tricks to make people _laugh_.
   - ● laugh
   - O cry
   - O run

19

Who saved the Key deer?

1   A Key deer is a small deer. It is about the size of a large dog. Sometimes it is called a "toy deer."

2   This deer lives in only one place in the world. That place is Florida.

3   In 1949, there were only 50 Key deer left. Soon they would all be gone. But 11-year-old Glen Allen wanted to save the deer. He and other people worked very hard. They did a good job. Now there are more than 800 Key deer.

Key deer

Fill in the circle (O) beside the right answer.

1. A Key deer is the size of a large _____.
   - O dog
   - O cat
   - O cow

2. This story does not tell about the _____ of Key deer.
   - O living place
   - O size
   - O food

3. In the third part of the story, what does the word *left* mean?
   - O went away
   - O a side
   - O still around

4. There are more than 800 Key deer now because people _____.
   - O ate them
   - O helped save them
   - O hid them

5. You can guess from the story that the Key deer is sometimes called a toy deer because of its _____.
   - O size
   - O color
   - O ears

What are stars like?

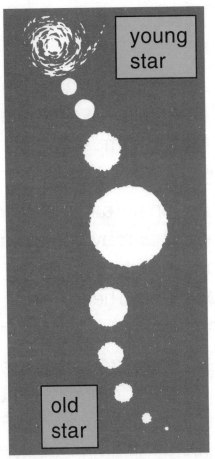

young star

old star

1   Have you ever wondered about the stars? In some ways, stars are like people. They are born. They grow old. And they die.

2   A star is born from dust and gas. Slowly the dust and gas make a ball. The ball gets very hot. Then it starts to give off light.

3   The young star grows into a giant. Many years go by. The older star begins to get small again. At last its light goes out. The star's life is over.

Fill in the circle (○) beside the right answer.

1. Dust and _____ make a star.
   - ○ gas
   - ○ snow
   - ○ rain

2. This story tells about _____.
   - ○ the life of a star
   - ○ old people
   - ○ the number of stars in the sky

3. In the first part of the story, what does the word *wondered* mean?
   - ○ moved
   - ○ looked at
   - ○ asked yourself

4. Stars give off light because they are very _____.
   - ○ small
   - ○ hot
   - ○ old

5. You can guess from the story that most stars are around for a _____ time.
   - ○ nice
   - ○ short
   - ○ long

What are tree frogs?

1   There are many kinds of tree frogs. A few live in water like other frogs. But most live in trees.

2   A tree frog can climb well. It can jump from tree to tree. It can even hang by one toe. A tree frog has a sticky pad on the end of each toe. These help the tree frog hold on.

3   Some tree frogs are about the size of your thumb. Others are as long as your hand. Tree frogs can be different colors, too. Most are green with spots of red, orange, or yellow.

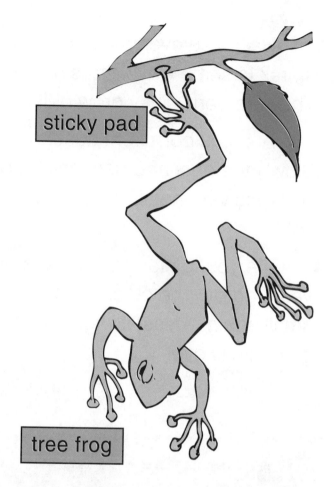

sticky pad

tree frog

Fill in the circle (○) beside the right answer.

1. Tree frogs live in _____.
   - ○ the ground
   - ○ trees
   - ○ ponds

2. This story tells about what tree frogs _____.
   - ○ eat
   - ○ are like
   - ○ see

3. In the second part of the story, what does the word *climb* mean?
   - ○ go up
   - ○ fall
   - ○ pretty

4. A tree frog can hang by its toes because it has _____ on them.
   - ○ sticky pads
   - ○ long nails
   - ○ dry leaves

5. You can guess from the story that tree frogs _____ a lot.
   - ○ eat
   - ○ swim
   - ○ move around

Who is Ruth Asawa?

Ruth Asawa

1   Ruth Asawa is an artist. Sometimes she makes things with wire. Sometimes she uses clay.

2   Ruth likes her friends. She likes to have them in her house. But her friends can't always be there.

3   That is why Ruth makes masks of clay. Each mask looks like one of her friends. The masks hang on a wall in her house. So far, there are more than 100 of them. "Only 9,000 more to go," says Ruth.

Fill in the circle (○) beside the right answer.

1. Ruth Asawa is _____.
   - ○ a doctor
   - ○ an artist
   - ○ a writer

2. This story tells mostly about the _____ that Ruth makes.
   - ○ masks
   - ○ baskets
   - ○ cakes

3. In the second part of the story, what does the word *have* mean?
   - ○ invite
   - ○ own
   - ○ catch

4. Ruth makes masks because she _____.
   - ○ wants to hide
   - ○ needs the wire
   - ○ likes her friends

5. You can guess from the story that Ruth Asawa _____.
   - ○ is also a teacher
   - ○ has a lot of friends
   - ○ cannot draw

What do fish doctors do?

1   Sometimes fish have cuts on their bodies. Little plants grow on the cuts. So the cuts do not get better. These fish need a doctor!

2   The wrasse is a "fish doctor." This fish cleans the cuts on other fish. It eats the little plants on them. This fish will even swim into another fish's mouth. Then it cleans the fish's teeth.

3   Some fish do not thank the wrasse for doing a good job. Sometimes they eat their doctor!

DR. WRASSE

fish doctor

Fill in the circle (○) beside the right answer.

1. The wrasse _____ the cuts on other fish.
     ○ cleans   ○ hurts   ○ makes

2. This story tells about a kind of fish _____.
     ○ worm   ○ doctor   ○ food

3. In the first part of the story, what does the word *get* mean?
     ○ become   ○ take   ○ grab

4. The cuts do not get better because little _____ grow on them.
     ○ fish   ○ fins   ○ plants

5. You can guess from the story that the wrasse _____ other fish.
     ○ doesn't like   ○ helps   ○ eats

Is corn a wild plant?

1   Corn was first used for food about 10,000 years ago. The Indians of Mexico gathered it from wild plants. Then about 7,000 years ago, things changed. The Indians learned how to grow corn for themselves. Soon corn spread all over North and South America.

2   The rest of the world didn't know about corn. Then in 1492, Christopher Columbus came here. He took corn seeds back to Spain. Before long, other explorers traveled around the world, too. They took corn with them.

3   Today corn is grown in almost every part of the world. But there are no longer any wild corn plants anywhere.

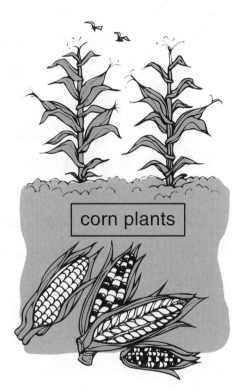

corn plants

Fill in the circle (○) beside the right answer.

1 Corn was first grown in _____.
   ○ Spain   ○ Mexico   ○ England

2. This story tells mostly about _____.
   ○ Indians   ○ Christopher Columbus   ○ corn

3. In the second part of the story, what does the word *rest* mean?
   ○ stop working   ○ everyone else   ○ take a nap

4. Corn grows all around the world because the _____ spread it.
   ○ explorers   ○ wind   ○ Indians

5. You can guess from the story that people almost everywhere _____ corn.
   ○ pop   ○ burn   ○ eat

What are flyways?

1   Most birds fly south in the fall. They go where there is food. The birds stay there until spring. Then they fly back north again.

2   Birds follow flyways on these trips. Flyways are like roads in the sky. People cannot see them. But the birds know where these roads are. Birds have used flyways for a long, long time.

flyways

SOUTH

>>>

Fill in the circle (○) beside the right answer.

1. Most birds fly _____ in the fall.
   ○ north   ○ home   ○ south

2. This story tells about the _____ that birds follow on their trips.
   ○ flyways   ○ people   ○ cars

3. In the first part of the story, what does the word *most* mean?
   ○ more than   ○ the best   ○ almost all

4. Most birds fly south in the fall because they can find _____ there.
   ○ roads   ○ food   ○ people

5. You can guess from the story that most birds stay in the north during the _____.
   ○ winter   ○ summer   ○ day

>>>

26

How long have people used pencils?

1   The word *pencil* comes from a Latin word. Long ago in Rome, a pencil was a thin brush with a fine point. The Romans used it for writing and drawing.

2   The Roman pencil made a thin, dark line. But the line was wet. People kept looking for a way to write with a dry line. It would be easier.

3   Finally, people in England found a way. In the 1500s, they found something dark under a tree. It was softer than stone. So it could be cut and shaped. This is the same lead that we use in our pencils today.

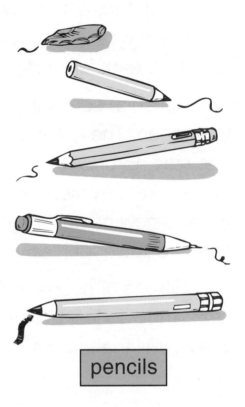

pencils

Fill in the circle (○) beside the right answer.

1. People have used pencils for _____.
   ○ a long time   ○ just a short time   ○ ever

2. This story tells about something we _____ with.
   ○ eat   ○ write   ○ play games

3. In the first part of the story, what does the word *drawing* mean?
   ○ playing games   ○ getting closer   ○ making pictures

4. The lead could be cut and shaped because it was _____.
   ○ soft   ○ heavy   ○ dark

5. You can guess from the story that writing with a _____ line is hard.
   ○ thin   ○ wet   ○ dry

Where can you find a leaning tower?

1   Long ago, a high tower was built. The tower was in the town of Pisa in Italy. It was a beautiful bell tower.

2   But soon something strange started to happen. The tower began to lean to one side. Each year, it leaned more and more. After a while, people gave the tower a new name. They called it the Leaning Tower of Pisa.

3   Millions of people visit Pisa every year. They go just to see the Leaning Tower. Will the tower ever fall? No one knows.

tower

Fill in the circle (○) beside the right answer.

1. The tower was built to hold _____.
   ○ bells   ○ animals   ○ stores

2. This story tells about a tower that _____.
   ○ is new   ○ fell down   ○ leans

3. In the second part of the story, what does the word *called* mean?
   ○ spoke on a phone   ○ named   ○ shouted

4. People go to Pisa in order to _____.
   ○ climb a hill   ○ ring a bell   ○ see the tower

5. You can guess from the story that _____.
   ○ most towers don't lean   ○ Italy is sunny
   ○ people are afraid of the Leaning Tower

What is a prairie dog town?

1   Prairie dogs are not really dogs at all. They are squirrels. They don't even look or act like dogs. But prairie dogs do bark like dogs. That is how they got their name.

2   Prairie dogs like to live near one another. So they dig their homes close together. Some of these "dog towns" are very big. More than 500 prairie dogs may live in the same town.

prairie dogs

Fill in the circle (O) beside the right answer.

1. Prairie dogs are really _____.
   O dogs   O squirrels   O cats

2. This story tells about the _____ of prairie dogs.
   O homes   O food   O puppies

3. In the second part of the story, what does the word *together* mean?
   O very happy   O well   O beside each other

4. Prairie dogs got their name because they _____ like dogs.
   O look   O sound   O act

5. You can guess from the story that prairie dogs _____.
   O are white   O live under the ground   O are really dogs

Who was Crispus Attucks?

1　Crispus Attucks was brought to America as a slave. He hated it. So one day he ran away. He spent many years working on ships at sea.

2　In 1769, Crispus came home to Boston. Back then, America was still part of England. English soldiers were in Boston. Many Americans were angry about this. They wanted America to be free. Crispus agreed.

Crispus Attucks

3　One night, Crispus and other Americans shouted at some English soldiers. Suddenly, shots rang out. Crispus was killed. Many African Americans died in America's fight to be free. Crispus Attucks was the first.

Fill in the circle (○) beside the right answer.

1. Where did Crispus die?
   - ○ on a ship
   - ○ on a farm
   - ○ in Boston

2. This story tells about a man who helped America become _____.
   - ○ rich
   - ○ poor
   - ○ free

3. In the first part of the story, what does the word *spent* mean?
   - ○ passed some time
   - ○ used money
   - ○ was tired

4. Because Crispus hated being a slave, he _____.
   - ○ ran away
   - ○ started a factory
   - ○ died

5. You can guess from the story that Crispus believed in _____.
   - ○ being a slave
   - ○ the English soldiers
   - ○ America

What is the fastest animal on land?

1 The fastest animal on land is the cheetah. It can win a race with a horse. A cheetah can even go as fast as some cars. It can run at up to 70 miles an hour.

2 The cheetah is thin. Its legs are long and strong. The cheetah cannot run very far. It gets too tired. But watch out for the cheetah in a short race. It will beat any animal on land.

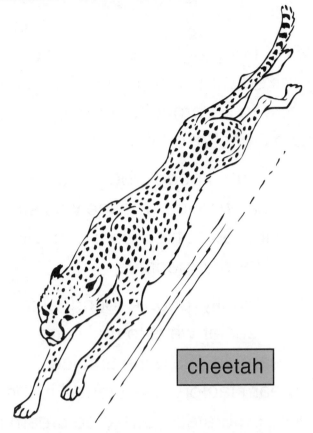

cheetah

Fill in the circle (○) beside the right answer.

1. The cheetah's legs are _____ and strong.
   - ○ long
   - ○ fat
   - ○ short

2. This story tells mostly about how _____ the cheetah is.
   - ○ fat
   - ○ fast
   - ○ golden

3. In the second part of the story, what does the word *beat* mean?
   - ○ hit
   - ○ lose
   - ○ run faster than

4. The cheetah cannot run very far because it gets _____.
   - ○ old
   - ○ tired
   - ○ cold

5. You can guess from the story that the cheetah is _____.
   - ○ not the fastest animal in the air
   - ○ the fastest animal in the whole world
   - ○ a beautiful cat

When was ice cream first made?

1   Long ago, kings ate fruit mixed with snow or ice. The snow had to be brought from far away. So it cost a lot of money.

2   Later, people began to eat cream with ice. The ice was still costly. So at first, ice cream was just for rich people.

3   Finally, people found faster and easier ways to make ice cream. In 1851, the first ice cream factory was started in the United States. Today, ice cream is for everyone.

ice cream

Fill in the circle (○) beside the right answer.

1. Long ago, ice cream was just for _____ people.
   ○ rich   ○ fat   ○ silly

2. This story tells how ice cream _____.
   ○ is sold   ○ tastes   ○ has changed

3. In the second part of the story, what does the word *just* mean?
   ○ fair   ○ only   ○ even

4. Ice cream is for everyone now because _____.
   ○ it costs less   ○ everyone is rich ○ it tastes good

5. You can guess from the story that ice cream is _____.
   ○ made with lemons   ○ good for you   ○ a cold food

32

What is an egg tooth?

egg tooth

1   A baby bird grows inside an egg. Its beak is very soft. So how does the bird get out of the egg? The baby bird uses its egg tooth.

2   The egg tooth grows at the end of the bird's beak. It is very small. But the egg tooth is hard. The baby bird uses it to break open the shell of the egg.

3   Before long, the egg tooth falls out. Most people never even know that the baby bird had one.

Fill in the circle (○) beside the right answer.

1. The beak of a baby bird is very _____.
   ○ large   ○ hard   ○ soft

2. This story tells how baby birds _____.
   ○ get out of their shells   ○ learn to fly
        ○ eat when they are first born

3. In the second part of the story, what does the word *hard* mean?
   ○ not easy   ○ not soft   ○ big

4. A baby bird can break open an egg because it has a hard _____.
   ○ tooth   ○ head   ○ toe

5. You can guess from the story that most people have never seen _____.
   ○ a baby bird   ○ a nest   ○ an egg tooth

What is a hand of bananas?

1   Bananas only grow in hot and wet places. The soil must be rich, too. Bananas don't grow on trees. They grow on high vines.

2   When a banana plant is about 10 months old, it blooms. Small flowers come out in bunches at the top of the vine. Each flower turns into a tiny green banana. These bunches of bananas are called *hands*. And each banana is called a *finger*. Five or more hands grow on each plant.

3   The bananas are picked when they are still green. They are shipped to markets far away. By the time the bananas get there, they are yellow. They are ready to eat!

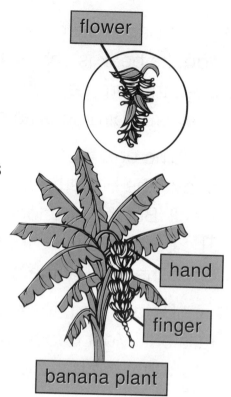

flower

hand

finger

banana plant

Fill in the circle (○) beside the right answer.

1. Each bunch of bananas is called a _____.
    ○ vine   ○ finger   ○ hand

2. This story tells mostly about how bananas _____.
    ○ grow   ○ look   ○ taste

3. In the first part of the story, what does the word *soil* mean?
    ○ make a mark on   ○ dirt   ○ use

4. Bananas need special weather, so they only grow where it is _____.
    ○ cold and wet   ○ hot and dry   ○ hot and wet

5. You can guess from the story that bananas should be _____ when you eat them.
    ○ yellow   ○ green   ○ brown

What are Gila monsters?

1   What is pink and yellow with black spots all over? A Gila monster!

2   Gila monsters are lizards. They live in hot, dry places. Gila monsters sleep under the sand during the day. Then they get up to hunt for food. Gila monsters eat the eggs of birds and snakes. They eat small animals, too.

3   Gila monsters are big. Some are almost two feet long. Their bite can make people very sick. Maybe that is why people call them monsters.

Gila monster

Fill in the circle (O) beside the right answer.

1. Gila monsters live where it is _____ and dry.
   - O cold
   - O cloudy
   - O hot

2. This story tells about a kind of _____.
   - O egg
   - O lizard
   - O pet

3. In the second part of the story, what does the word *dry* mean?
   - O not wet
   - O clean
   - O not funny

4. This animal may be called a monster because its bite can make people very _____.
   - O scared
   - O sick
   - O silly

5. You can guess from the story that Gila monsters are _____ animals.
   - O green
   - O small
   - O night

Who was the first woman doctor in the United States?

1   At one time, there were no women doctors in the United States. Many people thought that women should not be doctors. But Elizabeth Blackwell did not agree. She wanted to be a doctor. She wanted to help people.

2   Elizabeth Blackwell studied hard. In 1849, she became the first woman doctor in the United States. Dr. Blackwell spent her time caring for poor people. She also started a school to teach other women to be doctors.

Elizabeth Blackwell

Fill in the circle (○) beside the right answer.

1. Elizabeth Blackwell started a _____ for other women.
   - ○ house
   - ○ school
   - ○ park

2. This story tells about the first woman _____ in the United States.
   - ○ doctor
   - ○ teacher
   - ○ farmer

3. In the second part of the story, what does the word *started* mean?
   - ○ began
   - ○ jumped
   - ○ set out for

4. Elizabeth Blackwell became a good doctor because she _____.
   - ○ ran fast
   - ○ could not be a nurse
   - ○ studied hard

5. You can guess from the story that Dr. Blackwell proved that many people were _____.
   - ○ wrong
   - ○ sick
   - ○ old

What is a puffin?

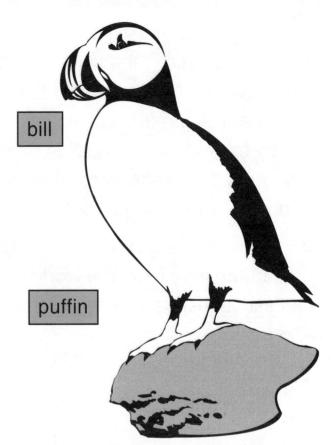

bill

puffin

1   Puffins would make good clowns. But you will not find them in a circus. You will find them near the sea. There they can swim and dive for fish.

2   A puffin is a bird with a fat, round body. Its face seems to be painted on. Each eye has a red ring around it. The large bill is yellow, red, blue, and black.

3   Many puffins have been killed by hunters. Now some people are trying to save these funny, friendly birds.

Fill in the circle (○) beside the right answer.

1. The puffin has a _____, round body.
   - ○ fat
   - ○ thin
   - ○ long

2. This story tells about a kind of _____.
   - ○ clown
   - ○ fish
   - ○ bird

3. In the second part of the story, what does the word *ring* mean?
   - ○ circle
   - ○ sound
   - ○ band around a finger

4. Many puffins have died because _____.
   - ○ hunters killed them
   - ○ people saved them
   - ○ they are funny birds

5. You can guess from the story that puffins look like clowns because of the _____ of their faces.
   - ○ shape
   - ○ colors
   - ○ size

What is the tallest animal in the world?

1 The giraffe is the tallest animal in the world. It is even taller than an elephant. A giraffe uses its tall body to get food. Its neck is 6 feet long. So the giraffe can eat leaves from the tops of high trees.

2 The giraffe also has long legs. It can run very fast. The world's tallest animal can run faster than a horse.

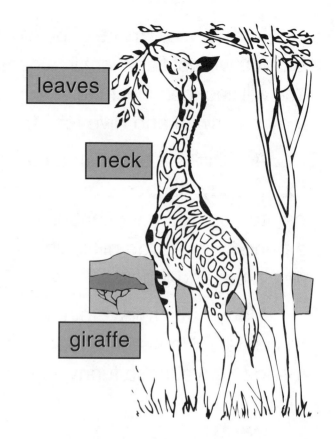

leaves

neck

giraffe

Fill in the circle (○) beside the right answer.

1. A giraffe eats _____.
   - ○ grass
   - ○ leaves
   - ○ lions

2. This story tells mostly about how _____ the giraffe is.
   - ○ tall
   - ○ young
   - ○ fat

3. In the first part of the story, what does the word *leaves* mean?
   - ○ goes away
   - ○ sets down
   - ○ parts of a tree

4. A giraffe can reach high trees because its _____ is very long.
   - ○ ear
   - ○ neck
   - ○ tail

5. You can guess from the story that its long legs help the giraffe _____.
   - ○ talk
   - ○ sleep well
   - ○ run fast

Who collects stamps?

1 More people collect stamps than any other thing. But they do not use these stamps to send letters. Instead, the people put them in special books. This keeps the stamps clean and safe. It's also an easy way to show off the stamps.

2 Stamps come in all sizes and colors. Some show birds or flowers. Other stamps show trains, ships, or airplanes. Many stamps show people who are well known, too.

3 Every country in the world makes stamps. And in every country, there are people who collect them.

stamps

Fill in the circle (○) beside the right answer.

1. How many countries make stamps?
   ○ none   ○ all   ○ about 20

2. This story tells about people who collect _____.
   ○ coins   ○ shells   ○ stamps

3. In the first part of the story, what does the word *letters* mean?
   ○ parts of words   ○ pieces of mail   ○ allowed

4. People put stamps in books in order to keep them _____.
   ○ clean   ○ hidden   ○ used

5. You can guess from the story that people like _____ their stamps.
   ○ others to see   ○ to send   ○ to tear

What is a dingo?

sheep

dingo

1   A dingo is a wild dog. It lives in Australia. Most dingoes are light brown with white feet. They have bushy tails.

2   These wild dogs eat meat. They often go hunting with their dingo family. Sometimes they kill sheep for food. Ranchers do not like the dingoes.

3   But some other people do. They keep the young dogs as pets. The dingoes make good hunting dogs, too.

Fill in the circle (○) beside the right answer.

1. Most dingoes are _____ with white feet.
   ○ black   ○ red   ○ brown

2. This story mostly tells about a kind of _____.
   ○ dog   ○ fox   ○ sheep

3. In the second part of the story, what does the word *sometimes* mean?
   ○ every day   ○ once in a while   ○ never

4. Ranchers do not like dingoes because the wild dogs _____.
   ○ make good pets   ○ sometimes kill sheep
                ○ have bushy tails

5. You can guess from the story that dingoes can be _____.
   ○ friendly to people   ○ larger than sheep
                ○ kept on a ranch

Who are smoke jumpers?

1   Forests are beautiful places. Animals live in them. People like to walk in them. But sometimes forests catch fire. Then fire fighters have to put out the fire.

2   Smoke jumpers are special fire fighters. They fight forest fires that are hard to reach. Often there are no roads near the fire. So the smoke jumpers jump into the forest from airplanes.

3   These fire fighters may be gone from home for days. They have to take food with them on the job. The brave smoke jumpers put out fires that no one else can.

smoke jumpers

Fill in the circle (○) beside the right answer.

1. Smoke jumpers get to the forest in _____.
   - ○ trucks
   - ○ airplanes
   - ○ cars

2. This story tells about people who put out _____.
   - ○ fires
   - ○ food
   - ○ floods

3. In the second part of the story, what does the word *reach* mean?
   - ○ grab
   - ○ grow
   - ○ get to

4. Smoke jumpers have to take food with them because they may _____.
   - ○ get tired
   - ○ be gone for days
   - ○ not need it

5. You can guess from the story that fighting fires is _____ work.
   - ○ easy
   - ○ quick
   - ○ hard

What is the biggest bird in the world?

1   An ostrich is the biggest bird in the world. It can grow to be 8 or 9 feet tall.

2   An ostrich has a small head. But its neck is very long. Its legs are long, too. This big bird can run very fast. It has to. The ostrich cannot fly.

3   Even a baby ostrich is big. After all, a baby ostrich comes from the biggest egg in the world. It is almost 8 inches long.

ostrich

Fill in the circle (○) beside the right answer.

1. The ostrich has a small _____.
   ○ neck   ○ egg   ○ head

2. This story tells mostly about the _____ of an ostrich.
   ○ legs   ○ size   ○ egg

3. In the second part of the story, what does the word *fast* mean?
   ○ far   ○ quickly   ○ close

4. An ostrich has to be able to run fast because the bird _____.
   ○ cannot fly   ○ has short legs   ○ is afraid of lions

5. You can guess from the story that an ostrich probably _____.
   ○ cannot see far   ○ eats bugs
          ○ does not have strong wings

Who needs dust?

1   Dust is tiny and dry. Bits of dust are too small to see. Yet dust is very important to us.

2   Winds carry dust everywhere. The wind passes over loose soil and rocks that are falling apart. From each place, it picks up dust. Then when the wind slows down, it drops the dust in a new spot.

dust

3   Too much dust can make people sick. So why do we need it? For one thing, dust in the air helps block the sun's strong rays. Even more important, dust makes rain and snow possible. Dust is at the center of every drop of water that falls from the sky.

Fill in the circle (○) beside the right answer.

1. Dust helps block the _____.
   ○ sun's rays   ○ snow   ○ loose soil

2. This story tells mostly about _____.
   ○ dust   ○ wind   ○ the sun

3. In the second part of the story, what does the word *picks* mean?
   ○ sharp tools   ○ gathers   ○ chooses

4. Dust is everywhere because _____ carry it.
   ○ ships   ○ rays   ○ winds

5. You can guess from the story that _____ are important to people.
   ○ rain and snow   ○ rocks   ○ new spots

What games do otters play?

1   Otters love to play games. These brown animals like to slide best of all. First they find a muddy hill near a river. Next they slide down the mud into the water. Splash! Then they climb up to the top and go down again.

2   Otters also like to race under the water. They play hide and seek, too.

3   Most baby animals like to play. In the otter family, everyone plays!

otters

Fill in the circle (O) beside the right answer.

1. Otters are _____ animals.
   - O brown
   - O young
   - O white

2. This story tells how otters like to _____.
   - O run
   - O eat
   - O play

3. In the first part of the story, what does the word *top* mean?
   - O a toy
   - O the highest part
   - O win

4. The otters find a muddy hill because they love to _____ it.
   - O slide down
   - O build
   - O hide under

5. You can guess from the story that otters like to _____ fast.
   - O eat
   - O swim
   - O work

Who was the birdman of the United States?

1   John Audubon lived many years ago. The United States was a new country then. People did not know much about its birds.

2   Then John Audubon went all over the country. He painted hundreds of pictures of birds. He also wrote about the birds. His pictures were very beautiful. The birds in them seemed to be alive.

3   People learned a lot from the pictures made by John Audubon. They began to call him the birdman of the United States.

Fill in the circle (O) beside the right answer.

1. People have learned about _____ from John Audubon.
   O other people   O birds   O trees

2. This story tells mostly about the _____ of John Audubon.
   O family   O pictures   O homes

3. In the first part of the story, what does the word *new* mean?
   O never used   O first   O young

4. John Audubon was called the _____ of the United States because he painted and wrote about birds.
   O birdman   O painter   O writer

5. You can guess from the story that John Audubon spent a lot of time _____.
   O outside   O in houses   O sleeping

Where do some animals go in the winter?

1   In the fall, bears eat as much food as they can. So do chipmunks and some other animals. They all grow very fat.

2   Then these animals look for a warm place away from the cold. They sleep in a cave or a hole all winter. They do not have to wake up to eat. They use their own fat for food.

3   At last, spring comes. The animals leave their winter resting places. Their long sleep is over.

chipmunk

bear

Fill in the circle (○) beside the right answer.

1. Animals that sleep all winter use their own _____ for food.
   - ○ fur
   - ○ homes
   - ○ fat

2. This story tells about animals that _____.
   - ○ eat leaves
   - ○ sleep all winter
   - ○ like caves

3. In the third part of the story, what does the word *spring* mean?
   - ○ a time of year
   - ○ jump
   - ○ a small river

4. In the fall, the animals grow fat because they _____ a lot.
   - ○ sleep
   - ○ eat
   - ○ run

5. You can guess from the story that these animals like the spring because it is _____.
   - ○ prettier
   - ○ longer
   - ○ warmer

How did yo-yos get their start?

1   Today the yo-yo is a toy. But once the yo-yo was for hunting. This early yo-yo was probably a rock. The rock was tied to a strong string. Hunters sat in a tree. They threw their yo-yos at an animal. If they missed, they could still pull their yo-yos back.

2   Yo-yo toys have been around for thousands of years. Children in the Philippines played with them. So did children in China and Greece. In the 1920s, yo-yos came to the United States. They were a big hit. And they still are.

yo-yos

Fill in the circle (○) beside the right answer.

1. The first yo-yos were used for _____.
   ○ playing   ○ singing   ○ hunting

2. This story tells about a hunter's tool that turned into a _____.
   ○ rock   ○ toy   ○ stick

3. In the first part of the story, what does the word *missed* mean?
   ○ wanted to see ○ did not hit   ○ left out

4. A hunter could get the yo-yo back because it _____.
   ○ did not cost much ○ always missed ○ was on a string

5. You can guess from the story that now most people _____ with yo-yos.
   ○ have fun   ○ hurt others   ○ hunt

What is a sloth?

1   A sloth is an animal with long hair. It lives in trees most of the time. This animal has long claws. It uses them to hold on to a tree branch. The sloth hangs upside down from the branch. It even eats and sleeps upside down.

2   A sloth moves very slowly. It can climb trees. It can swim, too. But a sloth cannot walk on its feet. It drags itself along.

3   Up in a tree, a sloth is hard to see. Little green plants grow in its fur. Their green color helps hide this strange, upside down animal.

claws

sloth

Fill in the circle (○) beside the right answer.

1. A sloth sleeps _____.
   ○ upside down   ○ while it eats   ○ on the ground

2. This story tells about an animal that _____.
   ○ walks quickly   ○ lives in trees   ○ cannot swim

3. In the first part of the story, what does the word *branch* mean?
   ○ part of a tree   ○ part of a road   ○ turn off

4. A sloth can hang from a tree because of its _____.
   ○ long hair   ○ big eyes   ○ long claws

5. You can guess from the story that sloths are easiest to catch _____.
   ○ in a tree   ○ in a river   ○ on the ground

What is a genie?

1   There is a story about a boy named Aladdin. He finds an old lamp. When he rubs it, up pops a genie (JEE-nee). The genie gives Aladdin three wishes.

2   Genies are not real, of course. The Arab people made them up long ago. The Arabs said that a genie had a body made of air or fire. Most of the time, a genie could not be seen. But sometimes a genie looked just like a person or an animal.

3   Some genies were good, like Aladdin's genie. Some genies were bad. These genies liked to play tricks on people.

genie

Fill in the circle (○) beside the right answer.

1. Genies are _____.
   - ○ people
   - ○ animals
   - ○ make-believe

2. This story does not tell about the _____ of genies.
   - ○ color
   - ○ looks
   - ○ bodies

3. In the first part of the story, what does the word *pops* mean?
   - ○ candy
   - ○ breaks
   - ○ comes out suddenly

4. Aladdin found a genie because he _____.
   - ○ told a story
   - ○ rubbed a lamp
   - ○ hit a table

5. You can guess from the story that the Arab people _____ genies.
   - ○ didn't like
   - ○ believed in
   - ○ killed

49

What are tickbirds?

1   Tickbirds are strange birds. They ride on rhinos. The rhinos like the tickbirds. These little birds eat bugs. So the tickbirds keep bugs off the rhinos' backs.

2   Tickbirds help the rhinos in another way, too. They tell the rhinos when to watch out. If trouble is near, the birds make a lot of noise. Tickbirds may be a rhino's best friend.

tickbird

rhino

Fill in the circle (○) beside the right answer.

1. Tickbirds ride on _____.
   - ○ birds
   - ○ rhinos
   - ○ bugs

2. This story tells about _____.
   - ○ hunters chasing rhinos
   - ○ strange bugs
   - ○ one animal helping another

3. In the first part of the story, what does the word *off* mean?
   - ○ not on
   - ○ covering
   - ○ close to

4. Tickbirds make noise when _____.
   - ○ they eat
   - ○ trouble is near
   - ○ rhinos run

5. You can guess from the story that tickbirds _____.
   - ○ need rhinos
   - ○ make good pets
   - ○ stay together

50

How do chuckwallas hide?

1 Chuckwallas are lizards. These animals live in hot, dry places. They like to sit on the hot rocks out in the sun. It keeps them warm.

2 When chuckwallas are afraid, they hide in a special way. They run into small cracks in the rocks. Then the chuckwallas fill themselves with air. This makes them very fat. Now nothing can pull the chuckwallas out of the cracks!

chuckwallas

Fill in the circle (○) beside the right answer.

1. Chuckwallas hide in the _____ when they are afraid.
   ○ sun   ○ air   ○ rocks

2. This story does not tell about where chuckwallas _____.
   ○ hide   ○ live   ○ play

3. In the second part of the story, what does the word *hide* mean?
   ○ put away   ○ get out of sight   ○ an animal's skin

4. Chuckwallas like the sun because it makes them _____.
   ○ warm   ○ hungry   ○ fatter

5. You can guess from the story that chuckwallas get _____ when they are filled with air.
   ○ wetter   ○ bigger   ○ warmer

What is in a camel's hump?

1   People drink water every day. A camel does not. A camel can go without water for a long time.

2   Some people think that a camel's hump is filled with water. That is not true. A camel's hump is filled with fat.

3   A camel uses the fat in its hump for food. So a camel can go without eating for a long time, too. What a strange animal the camel is!

hump

camel

Fill in the circle (○) beside the right answer.

1. A camel's hump is filled with _____.
   - ○ fat
   - ○ fur
   - ○ water

2. This story tells why a camel _____.
   - ○ drinks water
   - ○ can go without food
   - ○ can carry people

3. In the first part of the story, what does the word *every* mean?
   - ○ one
   - ○ the other
   - ○ each

4. A camel can go without eating for a long time because of its _____.
   - ○ mouth
   - ○ legs
   - ○ hump

5. You can guess from the story that camels are used a lot in _____.
   - ○ dry places
   - ○ big cities
   - ○ small farms

Where does lightning go?

1   Lightning flashes across the sky. It points down toward the earth. If the lightning hits a house or tree, it can start a fire. If it hits people, it can hurt them.

2   Some people use lightning rods. These are long metal poles. People put them high up on the roofs of their houses. A wire runs from the rod down into the ground.

3   Now lightning will not hit the house. It hits the rod instead. The lightning goes down the rod and down the wire. It ends up in the ground. Here, the lightning can't hurt anything.

lightning

rod

Fill in the circle (O) beside the right answer.

1. Lightning can start a _____.
   - O storm
   - O fire
   - O city

2. This story tells how to make lightning go _____.
   - O into the ground
   - O back to the sky
   - O away

3. In the second part of the story, what does the word *long* mean?
   - O wish for
   - O many years
   - O not short

4. People send lightning into the ground so that it _____.
   - O will not hurt anything
   - O burns the grass
   - O flashes across the sky

5. You can guess from the story that a lightning rod _____ a house.
   - O burns
   - O hurts
   - O saves

What is the smallest bird in the world?

1   Hummingbirds are the smallest birds in the world. One kind of hummingbird is only two inches long. It is also as light as a penny.

2   A hummingbird is very fast. It can fly straight up. It can fly straight down. It can even fly backward.

3   The wings of a hummingbird move very quickly. They beat 80 times in one second. You cannot see them move. But you can hear them. The wings make a humming sound.

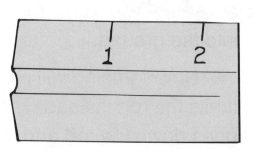

Fill in the circle (○) beside the right answer.

1. A hummingbird can weigh as little as a _____.
   ○ penny   ○ telephone   ○ ruler

2. This story tells about a _____ bird.
   ○ quiet   ○ slow   ○ tiny

3. In the first part of the story, what does the word *light* mean?
   ○ something that shines   ○ not heavy   ○ not dark

4. You cannot see the hummingbird's wings move because they _____.
   ○ make too much noise   ○ don't move at all
                    ○ move quickly

5. You can guess from the story that this bird got its name because its wings make a _____ sound.
   ○ roaring   ○ falling   ○ humming

What are dolphins?

1   Dolphins live in the sea. They are very smart animals. People can train dolphins to do tricks. They learn very fast.

2   Dolphins talk to each other. They do not use words. They talk in beeps. Some dolphins even try to talk to people.

3   Dolphins are friendly animals. Sometimes they help people in trouble in the water. They play games with swimmers, too. Dolphins are our best friends in the sea.

dolphin

Fill in the circle (○) beside the right answer.

1. Dolphins live _____.
   - ○ on land
   - ○ in rivers
   - ○ in the sea

2. This story tells mostly about how smart and _____ dolphins are.
   - ○ friendly
   - ○ big
   - ○ sad

3. In the second part of the story, what does the word *beeps* mean?
   - ○ short sounds
   - ○ words
   - ○ talks

4. People like dolphins because dolphins are _____.
   - ○ mean
   - ○ our friends
   - ○ pretty

5. You can guess from the story that dolphins are mostly not _____.
   - ○ good swimmers
   - ○ afraid of people
   - ○ smart animals

Who has your fingerprints?

1   In the 1880s, Sir Francis Galton found out something special. He learned that no two people have the same fingerprints. Not even twins have fingerprints that are alike.

2   Fingerprints are easy to take. Press your finger on a pad of ink. Now make a print on a piece of paper. Press your finger down very carefully. Roll it slowly from side to side. Do you see the lines and circles? That is your fingerprint.

3   Everyone has fingerprints. But no one else has yours!

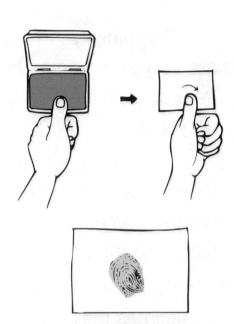

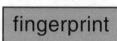

fingerprint

Fill in the circle (○) beside the right answer.

1. When did people find out about fingerprints?
   ○ 1770s   ○ 1880s   ○ 1990s

2. This story tells about _____.
   ○ fingertips   ○ fingerprints   ○ fingernails

3. In the second part of the story, what does the word *press* mean?
   ○ push down   ○ iron   ○ make a book

4. No one else has your fingerprints because everyone's are _____.
   ○ alike   ○ small   ○ different

5. You can guess from the story that if you leave a fingerprint on a chair, people can tell _____.
   ○ your hands were dirty   ○ what you look like
   ○ you were there